GW00383773

Information for Parents

In literacy lessons teachers will be seeking to encourage their pupils to:

• Read confidently and with understanding;
• Understand phonics and spelling patterns;
• Use neat handwriting with speed and accuracy;
• Expand their vocabulary;
• Appreciate a range of styles in fiction and poetry;
• Understand how stories are structured by the writers' use of settings, characters and plots;
• Read and use non-fiction materials;
• Develop their own writing using techniques of planning, drafting and editing;
• Enjoy reading books;
• Use imagination and inventiveness in their own writing.

Throughout the primary years the children will address their literacy work at three levels: word level, sentence level and text level.

Word level work includes word recognition, phonics, spelling, vocabulary and handwriting.

Sentence level work covers grammatical awareness, sentence construction and punctuation.

Text level work covers comprehension of reading and the composition of writing. It includes working with fiction, non-fiction and poetry.

Many schools operate a 'literacy hour' where they address all the aspects of literacy directly, but they will also seek to cover some aspects through other subjects throughout the school day.

In the **Literacy Now** series we provide practice materials for word level, sentence level and text level work, matched appropriately to children's ages. The books are designed to be used by parents working with their children to provide extra practice, whether out of a need to improve particular aspects of the children's progress or simply for the fun of working on English at home.

Literacy for ages 8–9

Excellent practice for literacy

You may prefer to use this book as a textbook, rather than as a book to write in. If so, you will need to use an exercise book for your answers.

Try to work out the type of answer that is required for each question. Some questions just need single words for their answers; others need whole sentences. We sometimes provide two or more lines to write answers on, to give you clues as to how much you ought to write.

If you need help from an adult it is all right to ask for it. Sometimes you can learn a lot more just by having a small amount of help. It is always a good idea to have your worked checked by an adult when you have finished it. If you have made mistakes you can learn from them.

Andrew Brodie

Codes

Ross had a rather unusual hobby. While his friends talked about football matches and their favourite TV programmes, Ross was busy learning about secret codes. He also took great delight in inventing codes of his own and felt this would help him greatly if he ever became a secret agent.

When he went on holiday, Ross wrote all his postcards in code (except the address, of course). The people who received them didn't always find out a great deal about the holiday, but they enjoyed trying to crack the code anyway.

He liked to put simple pictures in his writing to replace some of the words. This didn't always please his teacher. Sometimes he wrote words backwards. That pleased his teacher even less. During art lessons Ross would invent picture codes and in maths lessons he would experiment with number puzzles.

Ross had two favourite codes. One was a code in which he swapped the vowels in each word so that instead of 'a' he put 'e', instead of 'e' he put 'i', instead of 'i' he used 'o', for 'o' he wrote 'u', and then 'u' became 'a'. His other favourite code changed no letters but grouped them into threes. In this code sometimes there was a single or pair of letters at the end.

1 Why did Ross think that inventing codes might be useful?

_____

_____

2 On postcards, why did Ross <u>not</u> write the address in code?

_____

_____

3 What would Ross do during maths and art lessons?

_____

_____

4 Why was his teacher not pleased when Ross used codes in his writing?

_____

_____

Codes

5 The following sentences are written in Ross's favourite codes. Work out what they say and write them correctly.

Don ots tay upt ool ate ona sch ool nig ht.

_____

On my huasi O hevi e cet, e dug, end e hemstir.

_____

My fevuaroti prugremmi os un thi tilivosoun thos ivinong.

_____

Lon don ist hec api tal cit yof Eng lan d.

_____

Mys ist era ndI are goi ngs wim min gto nig ht.

_____

Present and past tenses

From the box, pick the word that is the past tense of each of the following words. The first one has been done for you.

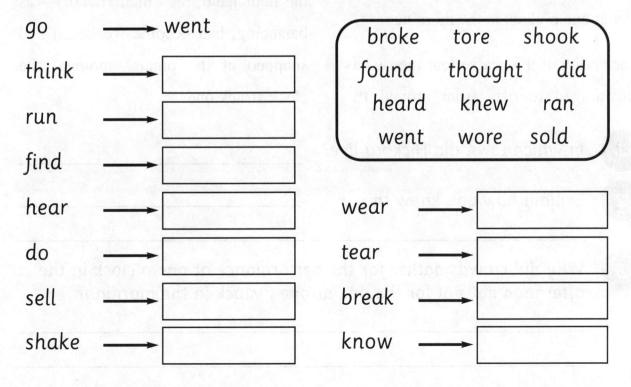

go ⟶ went

think ⟶ ☐

run ⟶ ☐

find ⟶ ☐

broke	tore	shook
found	thought	did
heard	knew	ran
went	wore	sold

hear ⟶ ☐   wear ⟶ ☐

do ⟶ ☐   tear ⟶ ☐

sell ⟶ ☐   break ⟶ ☐

shake ⟶ ☐   know ⟶ ☐

Town's Theatre Tragedy

The Rhymetown Herald is sad to report that Hickory, the world-famous mouse, died yesterday at exactly one o'clock in the afternoon.

Twice every day for the last ten months Hickory has been amazing crowds with his uncanny ability to sense when one o'clock is about to strike.

He made his home under an old grandfather clock that stands in the foyer of the town centre theatre. Shortly before one o'clock each afternoon many people gathered there to see Hickory run up the side of the clock. Theatre officials have also witnessed him performing this feat at one o'clock in the morning.

The ability of this marvellous mouse has encouraged tourists from around the world to visit our town to witness this strange phenomenon.

The exact cause of death has not yet been confirmed but it is rumoured that the hour hand, on which Hickory was balancing, had become weakened and snapped at the precise moment the clock struck one.

1 In which town did Hickory live? _____

2 Explain how you know this. _____

_____

3 Why did crowds gather for the performance at one o'clock in the afternoon but not for the one at one o'clock in the morning?

_____

_____

Death of famous mouse

4 What might have caused the hour hand of the clock to become weakened? _____

_____

_____

5 Which of the following words is nearest in meaning to <u>precise</u>?

precious   exact   dreadful   alarming

Suffixes

A suffix is a word ending.

Add the suffix <u>al</u> or the suffix <u>ary</u> to each of the following words to make a new word.

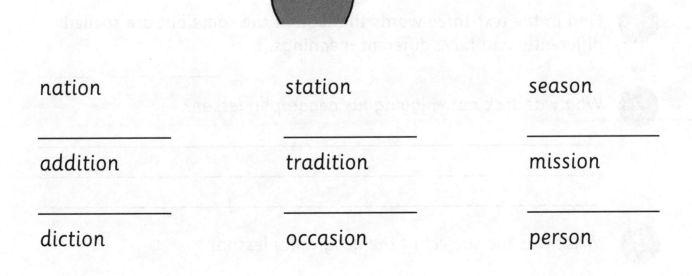

nation	station	season
addition	tradition	mission
diction	occasion	person

5

Jack's geography lesson

Jack was bored. He was in the classroom doing geography. Usually he enjoyed geography, but after a late night and then being woken early by his baby brother, today he was too tired to concentrate properly.

The lesson was about the climate in Britain. There were two pictures at the top of the worksheet and two more at the bottom. The four pictures represented the four seasons of the year. The teacher was talking about the differences between the pictures.

Jack walked out of the room and across the playground. He was confused. He couldn't recall the lesson ending, and why was it snowing at one end of the playground whilst his friends played in shorts and T-shirts at the other end? What was the tree doing standing in the middle of the netball court, and why, when it was covered in pink-scented blossom, was there a heap of brown fallen leaves around the base? This was most definitely a curious situation.

Jack felt a gentle shaking. Was it an earthquake? His eyes opened and, with some embarrassment, Jack realised he had been sound asleep and dreaming. The shaking had been his teacher waking him up, and the world outside the classroom was its usual self.

1 Find in the text three words that sound the same but are spelled differently and have different meanings.

                                           ___   __   ___

2 Why was Jack not enjoying his geography lesson?

_____

_____

_____

3 What was the subject of the geography lesson?

_____

Jack's geography lesson

4 In the text we are told 'Jack walked out of the room'. Did this really happen? Explain your answer.

_____

_____

5 Why did he see snow, blossom, warm sun and autumn leaves in the playground all at the same time?

_____

_____

6 Ring the word closest in meaning to <u>scented</u>.

white   stinking   falling   perfumed

Homophones are words that sound the same but are spelled differently and have different meanings.

Choose words from the box to complete the writing.

I have _____ bananas in the fruit bowl.

two	tail	to
pear	tale	
too	pair	

Put on a _____ of trousers.

I am taking my cat _____ the vets.

That story is a very good _____.

My dog has a long, black _____.

I would like to eat that juicy _____.

It is _____ cold to go out today.

7

The story of flying Robert

The poem below is by Heinrich Hoffmann.

He wrote children's poems with a message in them.

When the rain comes tumbling down
In the country or the town,
All good little girls and boys
Stay at home and mind their toys.
Robert thought, "No, when it pours,
It is better out of doors."
Rain it did, and in a minute
Bob was in it.
Here you see him, silly fellow,
Underneath his red umbrella.
What a wind! Oh! How it whistles
Through the trees and through the thistles!
It has caught his red umbrella;
Now look at him silly fellow,
Up he flies, to the skies,
No one heard his screams or cries;
Through the clouds the rude wind bore him,
And his hat flew on before him.
Soon they got to such a height,
They were nearly out of sight!
And the hat went up so high,
That it really touched the sky.
No one ever yet could tell
Where they stopped or where they fell:
Only this one thing is plain,
Bob was never seen again.

8

The story of flying Robert

1 Name the verb used instead of 'falling' that describes how the rain came down. _____

2 What is the shortened version of the name Robert? _____

3 Describe the rhyming pattern of the poem.

_____

_____

_____

4 Write three pairs of rhyming (or nearly rhyming) words found in the poem, that use different spelling patterns. (E.g. **great** and **mate** rhyme, but have different spellings.)

_____ _____ _____

_____ _____ _____

5 How do we know that Robert did not enjoy his flight?

_____

_____

6 What happened to Robert in the end?

_____

_____

7 What do you think is the message to be learned from this poem?

_____

_____

Arrange the words from the box into rhyming pairs.

sheet	store	claw	eight
clean	great	machine	beat

_____ _____ _____ _____

_____ _____ _____ _____

Holiday time

Patrice loved holidays. She loved being in the warm sun, staying in a hotel, being allowed to stay up late and swimming in an outdoor pool each day. Most of all though, Patrice enjoyed the special feeling of eating in real restaurants. The waiters taking her order, bringing her drinks and asking if she had enjoyed her meal, all made her feel very important.

Her parents and elder brother seemed quite casual about it but Patrice looked forward every day to the moment they would choose where to eat in the evening. She liked it best when they went to restaurants with an outdoor seating area so that she could watch the world go by as she ate. She also favoured restaurants with crisp white tablecloths and napkins folded into interesting shapes.

At home Patrice had a very special collection. It was a selection of menus given to her at some of the restaurants she had visited. She liked to look at them to be reminded of the holidays she had enjoyed so much.

1   Who did Patrice go on holiday with?

   _____

   _____

2   Name five things Patrice enjoyed about holidays.

   _____

   _____

   _____

   _____

   _____

3   Why did Patrice like eating in restaurants with outdoor seating areas?

   _____

   _____

4 What did Patrice collect?

_____

_____

5 Why did she enjoy looking at them?

_____

_____

Spelling

Some of Patrice's menus had some
words wrongly spelled.
Put right the 'crazy' menu below.

You may need
a dictionary to help
with this.

<u>Starters</u>
froot juice

_____

prorn cocktail

_____

lintel soup

_____

<u>Main Courses</u>
lamp chep

_____

<u>Main Courses</u>
roost beef

_____

chicken curly and rise

_____

cold mete and salad

_____

<u>Desserts</u>
I scream

_____

Rasberi pye and custard

_____

Recycling rap

Save all your glass
Recycle your waste paper
Down to the can bank
You should always caper

Buy cards that have come from
Sustainable woods
Always look out for
Recycled goods

Wash clothes and dishes
In an ecofriendly cleaner
Try walking to school
As car fumes are meaner

Turn off the taps
And waste no water
Keep the world clean
For your sons and daughters

One day they'll inherit
The world that you make
So keep it clean and healthy
For all their sakes.

1 In one sentence, sum up what the 'Recycling rap' is about.

_____

_____

2 Ring the word closest in meaning to the word <u>caper</u>.

    sprint   dance   rush   glide   walk

3 List four things named in the poem that should not be wasted or thrown away.

    _____   _____

    _____   _____

4 To be a 'rap' this poem should have a musical backing. Why do you think the poet called it a rap?

_____

_____

5 Explain the word <u>ecofriendly</u> found in verse 3.

_____

_____

Some of the verbs have been missed out of the following text.

Use words from the box to fill the spaces.

cried	hobble	told	hurt	be
left	vowed	crept	creaked	
go	ran	snapped	stepped	

The two children _____ quietly into the old dark house. They had been _____ never to ____ there as it might ___ dangerous.

The floorboards _____ as the children _____ carefully across them. Suddenly a board _____.

"Ouch!" _____ one of the children, "I've _____ my foot."

They _____ the house as quickly as possible.

One of the children _____ but the other could only _____.
They _____ never to go there again.

Steve's boring day

What shall I do today? thought Steve. It was only the second day of the school holidays and he was already bored.

He walked to the park, feeling rather fed up. He didn't notice the posters up advertising the opening of the new funfair.

Steve sighed and sat on the park bench. He didn't notice another poster offering free entry to the funfair for children under twelve years old.

Feeling more bored than ever, Steve went and bought an ice cream. He didn't hear his friends calling him to join them; they were on their way to the new funfair.

After kicking his heels in the park for over an hour, wondering wherever all his friends could be, he trudged wearily home.

What a boring time Steve had had. He felt sorry for his friends if their day had been as empty as his had been.

Now answer the questions on the next page.

14

Steve's boring day

1 What was the name of the central character in the story?

_____

2 What part of the school holidays was it? (Ring the correct answer)

near the beginning   the middle   near the end

3 Where did Steve go, hoping to meet his friends?

_____

4 While Steve was in the park, where were his friends going?

_____

5 Explain the phrase 'kicking his heels'.

_____

_____

6 Why did the author used the word 'trudged' to describe his walk?

_____

7 Had Steve's friends had an 'empty day'? Explain your answer.

_____

_____

Add <u>dge</u> or <u>ight</u> to each of the following to make 15 new words.

m_____   fl_____   he_____

fri_____   e_____   he_____

ple_____   fr_____   e_____

br_____   le_____   pl_____

bri_____   n_____   s_____

Exploration

In the late fifteenth and early sixteenth centuries a few brave sailors went on voyages of exploration. The sailing boats on which they travelled were only about twenty to thirty metres long, though at that time this was very long for a boat.

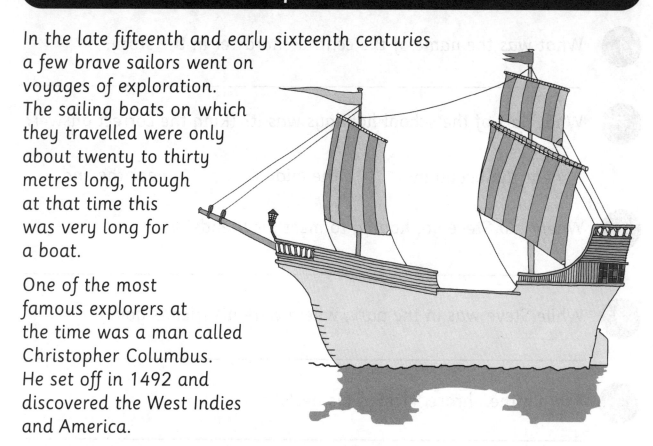

One of the most famous explorers at the time was a man called Christopher Columbus. He set off in 1492 and discovered the West Indies and America.

At the time he did not realise exactly where he was and believed he had reached India.

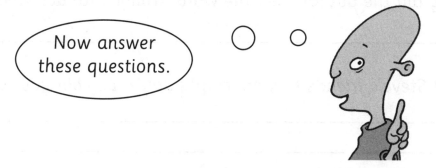

Now answer these questions.

1. Name the famous sailor that sailed on a voyage of discovery in 1492. _____

2. Did a large number of sailors go on voyages of exploration? _____

3. How do you know this? _____

_____

4. Where did Christopher Columbus believe he had landed?

_____

Adverbs

Adverbs are used to describe verbs.

Most adverbs have a 'ly' ending.

Look at this sentence:

She shouted angrily at the man.

Shouted is the verb and angrily is the adverb used to describe how she shouted.

Use adverbs from the box to describe the verbs below. Use each word only once.

whispered _____ _____

ate _____ _____

ran _____ _____

limped _____ _____

> quickly   secretively   steadily
>
> politely   quietly   painfully
>
> slowly   hungrily

Look at the following sentences. Underline the verbs in blue and the adverbs in red.

The boy walked wearily home.

My dog barks loudly when I arrive home.

The torch glowed dimly in the distance.

Horses eat hay noisily.

Rhyming couplets

Look at these poems by Robert Louis Stevenson.
The first verse of each poem is written below – you can find the complete poems in the poetry book called 'A Child's Garden of Verses'.

Picture Books in Winter

Summer fading, winter comes ~
Frosty mornings, tingling thumbs,
Window robins, winter rooks,
And the picture story books.

Summer Sun

Great is the sun, and wide he goes
Through empty heaven without repose;
And in the blue and glowing days
More thick than rain he showers his rays.

1 How many lines of poetry are in each verse? _____

2 What two seasons of the year are in the titles?

_____

3 How many syllables are in each line of 'Picture Books in Winter'?

_____

4 How many syllables are in each line of 'Summer Sun'?

_____

5 In 'Picture Books in Winter', why did the poet choose the words 'tingling thumbs'?

_____

6 In 'Summer Sun', explain the meaning of the word 'repose'. (You may need to use a dictionary to help you.)

_____

Rhyming couplets

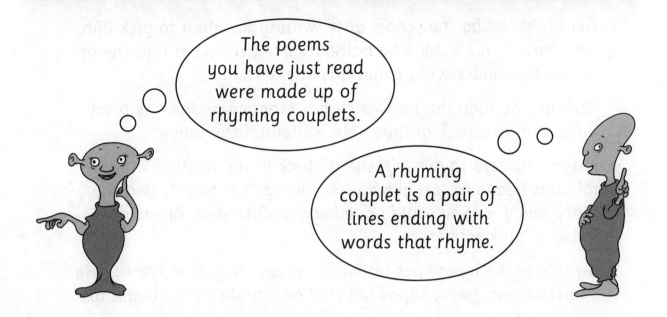

The poems you have just read were made up of rhyming couplets.

A rhyming couplet is a pair of lines ending with words that rhyme.

Choose words from the box to complete the rhyming couplets below.

bear   skip   seen

chair   dive   green

slip   sneeze

trees   five

I can run and I can _____
I am careful not to _____

Red and yellow, pink and _____
The brightest alien ever _____

One, two, three, four, _____
Ducks can swim and they can _____

I like to smell flowers, I like to smell _____
But I never smell pepper as it makes me _____

A little brown mouse was sitting on a _____
But he soon ran away when along came a _____

The wait

George stood by the school gate waiting for Mum to pick him up. Most of his friends had already been collected and George began to wonder what could have held Mum up.

Perhaps, he thought, her watch has stopped or she has been busy and lost track of time. He waited a little longer.

Maybe, he said to himself, she is stuck in the traffic. The minutes began to feel like hours. George's thoughts became more fanciful. She could have been abducted by aliens or foiled a bank robbery.

By this time, George felt rather alone and began to worry. Had something so awful happened that he couldn't even begin to imagine it?

Suddenly a car horn hooted – it was Mum.

✳ "Sorry I'm late dear," she said apologetically, "but the baby needed a nappy change just as I was about to leave home."

George smiled as he climbed into the car, pleased to see Mum but disappointed not to be hearing tales of bank robberies or aliens. Besides, he realised to his surprise, she had only been five minutes late!

Now answer the questions on the next page.

1 Explain the meaning of 'lost track of time'.

_____

2 Explain the meaning of 'George's thoughts became more fanciful'.

_____

_____

3 Look at the line of writing marked with a ✳ . Write the adverb found on that line. _____

4 Why was George surprised to realise that his mum was only five minutes late?

_____

_____

Alphabetical order

When words begin with the same letter we sort them into alphabetical order by looking at the second letter, then the third, etc.
Sort the following words into alphabetical order.

asteroid	antique	anchor	arch	angel
assembly	auction	amphibian	Australia	
Amazon	anniversary	annual		

1 _____   2 _____   3 _____

4 _____   5 _____   6 _____

7 _____   8 _____   9 _____

10 _____   11 _____   12 _____

Why do the words **Amazon** and **Australia** begin with capital letters?

_____

Write the word that means a type of sale in which people bid for goods.

_____

Incidents in the life of my Uncle Arly

Below is the first verse of this nonsense poem.

It was written in the 19th century by Edward Lear.

O my aged Uncle Arly!
Sitting on a heap of Barley
Thro' the silent hours of night,
Close beside a leafy thicket:
On his nose there was a Cricket,
in his hat a Railway Ticket
(But his shoes were far too tight).

Illustrate the verse in as much detail as possible.

Extending words

Many words can be extended, either at the beginning or at the end. This can change the meaning of the word.

For each question below, choose which of the words given could be put in the space in the sentence.

1. She looked quite _____ in her new dress.

    love   loving   lovely   unloved

2. Always try to do your work _____.

    proper   improper   properly

3. It is very _____ to kick anyone.

    kind   unkind   kindness   kindly

4. My _____ plays with me at school.

    friend   friendly   unfriendly   friendship

5. I am _____ whether or not I can go to the party.

    certain   certainly   uncertain   certainty

6. The stars shine _____ at night.

    bright   brightly   brightness   brighten

A view from my window

A class of Year 4 children were asked to write a paragraph entitled 'A view from my window'.

Here is what was written by two of them.

1

From the window in my bedroom I can see across our garden and over the road to the beach. On clear days the sea seems to stretch on forever and on misty days it seems like a ghostly nothingness.

Today is a clear day. I can see dad mowing the lawn for the first time since the winter, several people walking dogs along the wide sandy beach and a few fishermen sitting patiently waiting for a catch. There's not much traffic on the road yet but it will be busier once the summer season starts.

2

From my window I can see the houses across the road. Each side of the road is a wide grass verge with trees planted on it. The trees are just beginning to blossom and in a week or two will be covered in pink flowers.

Some of the houses are 'B & Bs' and the 'vacancies' signs have been hung at the windows ready to catch early tourists.

Ring the correct answers.

1 Which best describes the town the group of children live in?

A country village   A large city   A coastal resort

A view from my window

2 What time of year were the descriptions written?

    Spring   Summer   Autumn   Winter

Write the answers to the following questions.

3 Write down two things that helped you to know the season in which the texts were written.

_____

_____

4 What does it mean by 'B & Bs' in the second piece of writing?

_____

5 Write down four things you can see from your window. Ask an adult to check your spellings!

_____   _____

_____   _____

6 In the box below draw the view from one of the windows on the previous page.

Adjectives

Choose words from the box on page 27, to complete each list of adjectives.

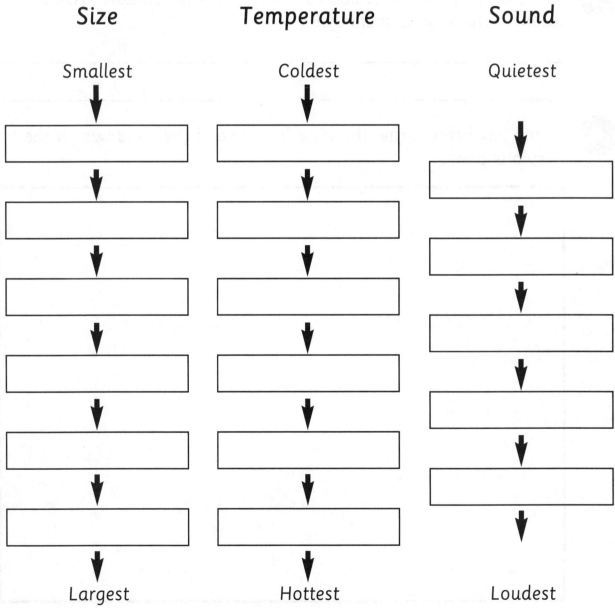

Size	Temperature	Sound
Smallest	Coldest	Quietest
↓	↓	↓
↓	↓	↓
↓	↓	↓
↓	↓	↓
↓	↓	↓
↓	↓	↓
↓	↓	↓
Largest	Hottest	Loudest

sprint   gigantic   mumble   shout   run
microscopic   icy   cool   boiling   warm
crawl   tiny   talk   whisper   cold   large
ecstatic   huge   happy   jog   bellow
walk   sad   small   hot   content   miserable

It may help to cross out the words as you use them.

Speed

Slowest

⬇

☐

⬇

☐

⬇

☐

⬇

☐

⬇

☐

⬇

Fastest

Mood

Happiest

⬇

☐

⬇

☐

⬇

☐

⬇

☐

⬇

☐

⬇

Saddest

Which is which?

Select words from the box to complete the puzzle.

adverb   consonant

noun   verb   comma

capital   exclamation

adjective   dictionary

Across
1. This describes a verb.
4. This sort of letter begins a sentence.
6. Use this to mark parts of a sentence, or to separate.
7. This mark is used for emphasis!

Down
1. This describes a noun.
2. A doing word.
3. Check your spellings here.
4. Not a vowel.
5. A naming word.

Punctuation marks

Join the clue to the correct answer.

Clue	Answer
,	exclamation mark
.	compound word
!	prefix
:	colon
;	vowels
e.g.	hyphen/dash
<u>con</u>firm	comma
blackboard	apostrophe
ra<u>tion</u>	suffix
a,e,i,o,u	abbreviation
-	semicolon
it's	full stop

Choose the correct abbreviation from the box.

```
e.g.    Mrs    a.m.    R.A.F.
R.S.V.P.      N.B.    V
p.m.    E.U.    M.P.
```

Royal Air Force   _____   after midday   _____

for example   _____   Member of Parliament _____

title of a married woman _____   versus   _____

before midday   _____   take note   _____

European Union   _____   please reply

Bodies

My outer shell's a delight to see,
Clear skin and bright eyes are on the outside.
Ten fingers, ten toes, arms waving, legs walking,
But what is encased I really must hide.

Heart is pounding and heavily thumping,
Muscles that bend and eyeballs that stare.
Teeth a-gnashing, tongue a-slurping,
Liver and kidneys all hidden with care.

Swirling bits with blood a-pumping,
Gibley things winding round and round.
Inside my head is a porridgy dumpling,
From the depths of my tummy come gurgling sounds.

The outside of my body is very attractive,
But oh what horrors are lurking within.
Most of the useful pieces inside me,
Look as if they should be thrown in the bin.

1 What does the author mean by 'outer shell'?

_____

2 Explain the word 'encased'.

_____

3 Name three 'major organs' from inside the body, mentioned in verse 2.

_____

4 What tells you that the writer either doesn't know, or chooses not to use, the names of some internal body parts?

_____

_____

5 How is the brain described?

_____

6 What is slightly different about the rhyming pattern in verse 3?

_____

_____

Synonyms

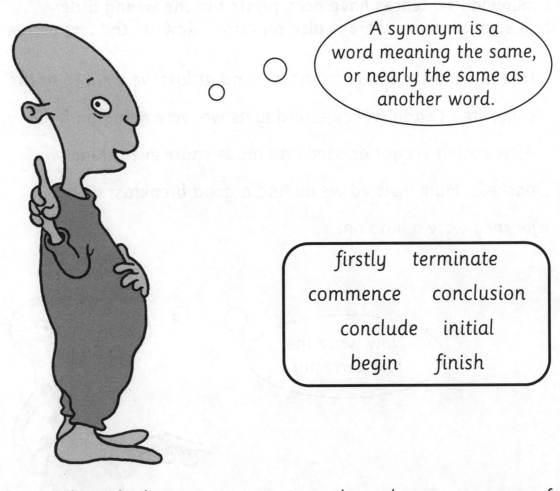

A synonym is a word meaning the same, or nearly the same as another word.

firstly   terminate

commence   conclusion

conclude   initial

begin   finish

Split the words in the box into two sections, those that are synonyms for start and those that are synonyms for end.

Start

_____

_____   _____

_____   _____

_____   _____

End

Order, order!

The following sentences have been printed in the wrong order.
Within each sentence there is also an error. Rewrite the text correctly.

Dad hitched the trailer to the car and at last we were of to the campsite. I early woke yesterday as we were going on holiday. After eating we got dressed and made shure everything was packed. Mum insisted we all had a good breakfast as the journey were a long one.

Now write the text correctly.

_____

_____

_____

_____

_____

_____

_____